THIS BOOK
BELONGS TO

....

....

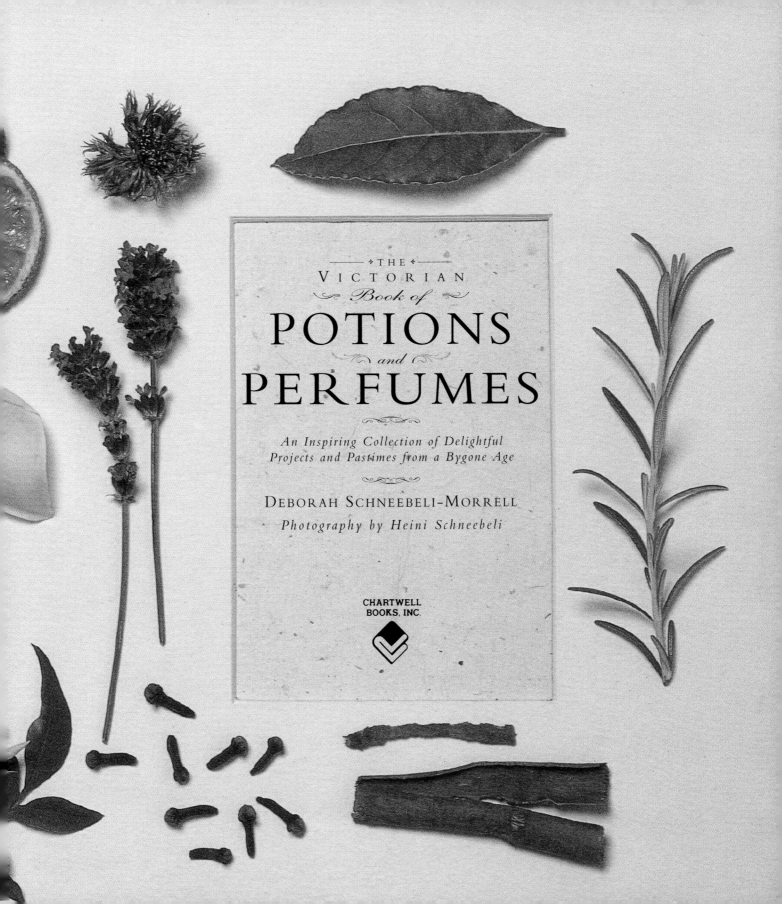

THE · VICTORIAN ·

Book of

POTIONS

and

PERFUMES

An Inspiring Collection of Delightful
Projects and Pastimes from a Bygone Age

DEBORAH SCHNEEBELI-MORRELL

Photography by Heini Schneebeli

CHARTWELL
BOOKS, INC.

The Victorian Book of
Potions and Perfumes

Designed and created by
THE BRIDGEWATER BOOK COMPANY LTD

Art Director: Peter Bridgewater
Designer: Jane Lanaway
Editor: Geraldine Christy
Managing Editor: Mandy Greenfield
Photography: Heini Schneebeli
Page makeup: Chris Lanaway

CHARTWELL BOOKS
A division of Book Sales, Inc.
114 Northfield Avenue
Edison, NJ 08837 USA

CLB 4087
© 1995 CLB Publishing, Godalming, Surrey
All rights reserved.
Color separation by HBM Print Ltd, Singapore
Printed and bound in Singapore by Tien Wah Press

ISBN 0-7858-0380-7

CONTENTS

INTRODUCTION

*W*E ALL look back with affection and nostalgia to the Victorian era of a hundred or so years ago when domestic creativity flourished.

Middle-class women were accomplished in what were referred to as drawing-room skills. These included watercolour painting, all manner of papercrafts, collecting and assembling seaweeds, and pressing flowers into beautiful floral albums. They practised penmanship, stitched and embroidered clothes, quilts and fancy work and enthusiastically embraced the new craze of découpage.

Older domestic skills, such as making perfumes, toiletries and cosmetic preparations as well as culinary knowledge, were in the domain of the housekeeper. She had a wide-ranging knowledge, not only of cookery but of the uses of herbs and flowers. It was she who prepared and kept the store room full of jams, pickles, preserves and bottled fruit.

A well-stocked and maintained garden was most important. The larger gardens not only supplied vegetables for the table, but provided large quantities of herbs and flowers, to be used for cooking or fresh flower arrangements in the house, or for drying as essential ingredients for pot pourris; see the recipe for the traditional Victorian pot pourri on page 15. Dried flowers were also made into attractive papery floral displays throughout the house, particularly during the winter months when fresh flowers were scarce.

Infusions were made from petals and distilled into fragrant flower waters, widely used in the kitchen as well as vital ingredients in homemade cosmetics. Rosewater was a particular favourite and adds its sweet fragrance to the rose and glycerine cleansing cream on page 13 and the rose and violet perfume on page 25. Try making the subtly flavoured rose petal jam on pages 40–1, a truly exotic preserve that deserves to be revived.

Throughout history herbs have been used for culinary purposes. The recipes on pages 26–7 for flavouring oil and vinegar with rosemary and tarragon are well-tried favourites that are simple to make.

Other culinary recipes include a sparkling elderflower drink on page 35, a real old-fashioned favourite, with a low alcohol level. For a special occasion serve the impressive dessert Rhumtopf described on page 37, a rich and extravagant way of preserving soft fruits in sugar and white rum.

If you possess some treasured pieces of furniture, try making the lavender-scented furniture polish on pages 42–3 and fill your home with this distinctive perfume.

All the projects in this book have been inspired by the diligent and adventurous spirit of the Victorian era. They are simple to follow and the ingredients are widely available.

 *I*N THE Victorian home an impressive variety of
toiletries and remedies in the form of perfumes, flower
waters, pomanders, bath oils and tonics were prepared by
the housekeeper with the assistance of the still-room maid.
Fresh ingredients were provided by the head gardener from
a well-stocked garden.

ORANGE FLOWER WATER TONIC

*T*his tonic makes a refreshing treatment for tired and ageing skin, as it stimulates the growth of healthy new cells.

INGREDIENTS

170 ml (6 fl oz) orange flower water

115 ml (4 fl oz) witch hazel

5 drops of glycerine

5 drops of neroli essential oil

Lidded glass jar or bottle

Photocopies of small black and white engravings

Ribbons in associated pastel shades

1 *Put all the ingredients into the lidded jar or bottle, and shake vigorously to blend together.*

2 *Decant into pretty bottles with airtight stoppers.*

*O*range blossom is, as we all know, a lucky flower at a wedding. Some say it will ensure the union will be blessed with the patter of tiny feet.

Old English Omen

3 *Cut out the black and white photocopies into little labels and attach to the bottles with ribbons tied into decorative bows.*

ROSE AND GLYCERINE CLEANSING CREAM

*T*he gentle soothing qualities of this rose-scented cleansing cream make it ideal for removing the dirt and make-up of a busy day.

INGREDIENTS

Double saucepan

35 ml (1½ fl oz) almond oil

15 ml (1 tablespoon) glycerine

30 ml (2 tablespoons) lanolin

30 ml (2 tablespoons) beeswax

Glass fireproof basin

Small saucepan

Sauce whisk

Large pinch of borax

45ml (3 tablespoons) rosewater

5ml (1 teaspoon) zinc oxide cream

7 drops of rose essential oil

*L*ove is a secret like a bird in a shell like a rose ere it blossom All unseen will it dwell.

JOHN CLARE
1793–1864

1 *In a double saucepan slowly heat the almond oil and glycerine together. Put the lanolin and beeswax into the glass basin over a pan of hot water. Mix together. Pour the oil and glycerine mixture into this and beat with the sauce whisk.*

2 *Dissolve a large pinch of borax in slightly heated rosewater. Add to the lanolin, wax and oil mixture, beating all the time to achieve a cream-like consistency. Allow to cool.*

3 *When cool finally beat in the zinc oxide cream and the rose oil. Spoon into pretty jars and label.*

*How well the skilful gardener drew
Of flowers and herbs this dial new;
Where from above the milder sun
Does through a fragrant zodiac run;
And, as it works, the industrious bee
Computes its time as well as we.
How could such sweet and wholesome hours
Be reckoned but with herbs and flowers.*

The Garden
ANDREW MARVELL 1621–78

POT POURRI

NOTHING IS more evocative of a garden
in high summer than a pretty bowl of richly
scented pot pourri displayed in every room. For
Victorian women, already so industrious
and inventive with other flower crafts,
the collection, drying and
preparation of flowers and herbs
for a variety of recipes was an
enjoyable and practical pastime.

TRADITIONAL VICTORIAN POT POURRI

INGREDIENTS

1 teaspoon allspice

30 g (1 oz) orris root

2 drops of rose oil

2 drops of lavender oil

3 drops of cottage garden mixture oil

1 litre (2 pt) mixed garden flowers – chamomile, rosebuds and petals, larkspur, honeysuckle, marigold, hydrangea

75 g (2½ oz) mixed sweet herbs – sweet-cicely, lemon verbena, scented geranium leaves

25 g (¾ oz) lavender

Handful of lavender heads to decorate

1 cinnamon stick

1 tablespoon whole cloves

*O*nce you have some experience of making pot pourris, try inventing your own recipes using flowers from different seasons. Create a freshly scented bowl of spring flowers with fragrant lily of the valley for a pretty bedroom, or a richly spiced and opulent winter pot pourri for a Christmas display. Change the colour combinations to suit your room decoration.

1 In a small bowl mix together the allspice, orris root and essential oils (rose, lavender and cottage garden).

2 Rub the mixture between your fingers, making sure that the oil penetrates the mixture evenly.

3 Mix together all the remaining ingredients in a large bowl. Break the cinnamon stick into small pieces. Remember to put aside some rosebuds, petals, lavender heads and hydrangea to decorate the finished pot pourri.

4 Add the mixture of fixative (the orris root, spices and oils) to the bowl of dry ingredients. Stir together to produce an evenly scented mixture.

5 Put the mixture in an airtight container and store in a dark place for three weeks, occasionally shaking the container. The longer you leave the mixture, the stronger the fragrance will become. Eventually remove from the container and display in a beautiful blue and white china bowl.

*Two hairs on your shoulder
are better than one,
As two means a letter, and one means none.*

Old English Proverb

HAIR TOILETRIES

*I*N THE nineteenth century women took pride in styling their hair beautifully, grooming it with typical Victorian attention to detail. With the help of a lady's maid it was washed, conditioned, scented and strengthened with all manner of preparations. These were expertly concocted by the housekeeper from a combination of natural ingredients picked from the garden by the head gardener and more unusual products that were widely available from the local pharmacy. Rosemary, an aromatic sun-loving herb, is easy to grow and popularly cultivated in many gardens; it is a natural conditioner and an ideal herb for hair care.

ROSEMARY SHAMPOO

*T*he addition of fresh rosemary to this gentle shampoo helps to condition and strengthen hair. It has been used throughout the ages as a well-tried herb for stimulating hair growth.

INGREDIENTS

1 bunch of fresh rosemary

300 ml ($\frac{1}{2}$ pt) of distilled water

125 ml (4$\frac{1}{2}$ fl oz) bottle unscented shampoo (baby shampoo is ideal)

4 drops of rosemary essential oil

2 Strain the rosemary decoction into a large screw-topped jar, add the unscented shampoo and 4 drops of essential oil, then shake well to mix.

1 Put the fresh rosemary in a saucepan with the distilled water. Bring to the boil and simmer for half an hour, reducing the amount of liquid by half to 150 ml ($\frac{1}{4}$ pt). Allow to cool.

3 Decant into pretty bottles.

ROSEMARY AND LAVENDER HAIR MASSAGE OIL

*N*ourish your hair and add lustre to it with this fragrant oil. To use the oil, warm it slightly, then massage it into the hair vigorously with your fingers. Comb it out and leave for 30 minutes. Wash off with rosemary shampoo.

INGREDIENTS

125 ml (4$\frac{1}{2}$ fl oz) almond oil

3 drops of rosemary essential oil

3 drops of lavender essential oil

A rosemary bush will mature and grow old, Only where a woman heads the household.

Old English Proverb

1 In a small jug, mix the almond oil with the essential oils.

2 Decant into pretty bottles.

SCENTED CANDLES

~ ❦ ~

Wax candles were expensive and used sparingly in all but the grandest houses. The ordinary household made do with the failing light of evening for as long as possible. It was not uncommon for wax and tallow candles to be made by the ever-industrious housekeeper. The best candles were brought out for special occasions or when guests were expected. These unusual scented floating candles arranged amongst fresh flowerheads make an elegant centrepiece to a table setting.

MATERIALS

500 g (1 lb) paraffin wax

Double saucepan

Wax dye discs in pink and orange

Wax perfume or essential oils – rose and gardenia

Tin miniature tartlet cases in assorted sizes

50 cm (18 in) primed wick

A number of flat-headed flowers – roses, marigolds or gardenias

TO THE WIFE WHO HAS TO PROVIDE ON VERY SLENDER MEANS

Take care that your table-linen is spotlessly pure and white, the cloth well pressed, that you have table napkins and finger glasses for dessert. These little elegancies cost next to nothing and add immensely to the air of comfort and refinement which your table should possess. In summer, manage if possible to have a centre ornament of candles and flowers, if only a cheap vase.

Warnes Model Cookery and Housekeeping 1869

1 Put the paraffin wax into the double saucepan. Heat the water in the bottom pan and the wax will slowly melt.

2 Add a small piece of the wax dye disc to colour the wax; the more dye, the deeper the colour.

3 Add a few drops of wax perfume or essential oil.

4 Pour the melted wax carefully into the moulds and allow to set slightly.

5 Cut the wick into 5 cm (2 in) lengths and push each piece into the centre of the setting wax. As the wax begins to harden, it will shrink a little. It may be necessary to 'top up' the candle with a little more molten wax.

6 Release the candles from the moulds and intersperse with flat-headed flowers in an elegant dish filled with water.

The fairest things have fleetest end,
Their scent survives their close:
But the rose's scent is bitterness
To him that loved the rose.

DAISY FRANCIS THOMPSON
1859–1907

BATH OILS

DURING THE nineteenth century there were great developments in plumbing and sanitation, and permanently installed baths became more common. The strenuous task of filling the baths with hot water was allotted to the servants of the house. The Victorians believed that taking regular baths braced the body and enlivened the spirit, promoting health, cleanliness and free circulation of the blood.

PENNYROYAL BATH VINEGAR

A refreshing and antiseptic bath preparation. Use one cupful per bath.

INGREDIENTS

275 ml (½ pint) cider vinegar
275 ml (½ pint) water
One handful of pennyroyal
One handful of lemon balm

NEROLI AND CHAMOMILE SCENTED BUBBLE BATH

*N*eroli essential oil, extracted from fragrant orange blossoms, is well known for its healing qualities; it is the main ingredient in this soothing bubble bath.

1 Add 10 drops of neroli and 5 drops of chamomile essential oil to 180 ml (6 fl oz) of unscented mild baby bath liquid.

2 Pour under the hot tap when the bath is running and relax in the soothing fragrance.

1 Bring the vinegar and water to the boil in a large saucepan.

2 Add the herbs, remove the pan from the heat and cover with a lid. Leave to steep overnight.

3 Strain the infusion into a screw-topped jar. Shake well and decant into decorative bottles. Use within one or two weeks.

O Beauty, passing beauty! sweetest Sweet!
How can'st thou let me waste my youth in sighs?
I only ask to sit beside thy feet.
Thou knowest I dare not look into thine eyes.

Poems
ALFRED, LORD TENNYSON 1809–92

A TRADITIONAL
HERBAL FOOT BATH

*T*his is an effective therapeutic treatment to
soothe and refresh aching feet.

*1 Add a generous
handful of lavender and
spearmint with a handful
of sea salt to a large bowl
of water.*

*2 Immerse the feet in
this for at least 10
minutes and your whole
being will feel revived.*

*If you could see
my legs when I take
my boots off, you'd form
some idea of what
unrequited affection is.*

Mr Toots
Dombey and Son
CHARLES DICKENS
1812–70

REJUVENATING
BATH OIL

*S*prinkle a few drops of this fragrant oil into
your bath after a tiring day.

*1 To 180 ml (6 fl oz)
of base dispersing oil add
5 drops each of lavender,
rosemary and juniper
essential oil.*

*2 Store in pretty
bottles and add a small
quantity to your bath
to revitalize you.*

ROSE AND VIOLET

*V*ICTORIAN LADIES were passionate about flowers. They studied botany in childhood and set about assembling stunning collections of pressed flowers, arranging them delightfully in beautifully bound albums. Flowers became all-pervasive in designs for all manner of items. Communication through symbolism, aided by the many editions of the popular little book, *The Language of Flowers*, became a common means of expression.

PRESSED VIOLET GREETINGS CARD

MATERIALS

Handmade natural paper 11 × 18 cm (4$^1/_2$ × 7 in)

Pressed violet with leaves

Rubber-based glue for plant material

Toothpicks for applying glue

50 cm (20 in) paper lace ribbon

Paper glue

Small scissors

50 cm (20 in) of faded violet satin ribbon 1 cm ($^1/_2$ in) wide

---

PRESSED FLOWERS

*I*t takes about two weeks to press flowers successfully. If you do not have a flower press, just lay your specimens carefully between absorbent paper within the pages of a heavy book.

---

1 Fold the paper neatly in half lengthways to make a stand-up card.

2 Carefully place the pressed violet in position on the front of the card, then remove and place little dabs of rubber glue with the toothpick on the card where the violet leaves and stalk will appear. Press the flower in place and allow the glue to dry.

3 Cut the paper lace ribbon to trim the outside edges of the card. Glue in place with paper glue.

4 Finally, make two slits along the fold of the card, thread the satin ribbon through and tie into a pretty bow. You may also like to write the botanical name beneath the pressed flower.

*T*he Victorians excelled in the domestic production of fragrant floral waters, and most households produced the well-known favourites of lavender, rose and violet. Floral waters and essential oils are widely available today and it is surprisingly simple to make lovely naturally scented perfumes with them.

ROSE AND VIOLET PERFUME

INGREDIENTS

125 ml (4$^1/_2$ fl oz) rosewater

75 ml (2$^1/_2$ fl oz) violet toilet water (or, if this is difficult to obtain, 10 drops of Devonshire violet perfume mixed with 30 ml (1 fl oz) eau de Cologne)

10 drops of rose essential oil

125 ml (4$^1/_2$ fl oz) vodka

1 Mix all the ingredients together in a china jug.

2 Decant into pretty glass perfume bottles with glass stoppers.

HERB OIL AND VINEGAR

*D*URING THE nineteenth century recipe books abounded with advice on the varied uses of herbs both in the kitchen and the sick room, and to this day they are eaten for their flavour and are widely used for medicinal purposes. These decorative moulded glass bottles filled with herb-flavoured oil and vinegar would look attractive on your kitchen shelves. Simple to produce, with their decorative sealed corks they would also make a special gift for an enthusiastic cook.

ROSEMARY OIL

INGREDIENTS

Basin

Fresh rosemary

1 litre (2 pt) olive oil

Muslin

Moulded glass bottle with cork

Sealing wax

Blue ribbon

1 Loosely fill a basin with 2 handfuls of freshly gathered rosemary.

2 Pour 1 litre (2 pt) of good olive oil over the fresh herbs. Cover with muslin and put in a warm airy place; a sunny windowsill is ideal. Allow to steep for two weeks and stir daily.

3 Strain through muslin and decant into a moulded glass bottle in which you have previously inserted a sprig of fresh rosemary.

4 Place the cork in the top of the bottle. Seal with a coin on the hot sealing wax. Cut a length of ribbon and place around the neck of the bottle, drip sealing wax onto the place where the ribbons cross on the front of the bottle, then make an impression with the coin.

HOW TO SEAL

1 Drip the lighted sealing wax onto the tops and sides of the cork.

2 While the wax is still soft, press a coin onto the top of the cork to make an impression.

TARRAGON VINEGAR

INGREDIENTS

Fresh tarragon

1 litre (2 pt) screw-topped jar

1 litre (2 pt) cider vinegar

Muslin

Moulded glass bottle with cork

Sealing wax

Ribbon

1 Pick 2 handfuls of fresh tarragon and pack loosely into 1 litre (2 pt) screw-topped glass jar.

2 Heat 1 litre (2 pt) of cider vinegar, making sure it does not boil, and pour over the fresh herbs. Screw on the lid and place the jar in a warm dry place. Shake the jar every day for two weeks.

3 Strain the liquid through muslin and decant into a moulded glass bottle to match the herb oil. Push a sprig of fresh tarragon into the bottle.

4 Cork the bottle and seal with sealing wax, making an impression with a coin into the hot wax on the top of the cork. Cut a length of ribbon and place around the neck of the bottle, drip sealing wax onto the place where the ribbons cross and seal with a coin.

*T*he use of vinegar
is recommended when
an overdose of strong
wine, spirit, opium, or
other narcotic poisoning
has been taken.

The Complete Servant
SAMUEL AND SARAH
ADAMS 1825

OVEN GLOVES

❧ ✦ ❧

UNTIL THE middle of the nineteenth century when more sophisticated kitchen ranges began to be installed with a cast-iron oven on one side and a boiler heater on the other, most of the cooking was done over an open fire. There was a strict hierarchy in the kitchen. It was the cook who planned and prepared the meals and supervised the pantries and storerooms. The scullery maid's job was to black-lead and light the kitchen range early in the morning in preparation for the hard work of the day. These practical oven gloves will add an atmosphere of nostalgia to the most modern of kitchens; they have lemon balm and cloves sewn into the padding, so they release their scent when warm.

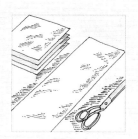

1 Cut one length of cotton interlining 80 × 17 cm (32 × 7 in). Cut four pieces 17 cm (7 in) square.

MATERIALS

50 cm (20 in) cotton interlining	Large handful of lemon balm
Scissors	40 cm woven light upholstery fabric
Needle and thread	2.5 m (8 ft) bias binding in matching colour
Large handful of whole cloves	2.5 m (8 ft) cotton fringed braid

2 Make two pockets with the four pieces of cotton interlining by sewing up three sides. Fill loosely with whole cloves and lemon balm leaves. Tack loosely across the 'pockets' to hold the spices in place. Close the open side.

3 Lay these herb and spice filled pockets onto either end of the longer strip. Tack in place.

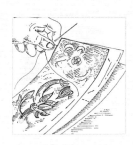

4 Cut two lengths of the upholstery fabric 17 × 80 cm. Place the cotton interlining with spice-filled pockets between these two lengths; tack in place.

5 Cut two lengths of fabric 17 cm (7 in) square and, with reverse side showing, bind one edge with bias binding, lay onto each end of the gloves, and tack in place, leaving bound edge free for hands to go in.

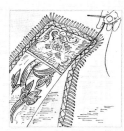

6 Bind around the perimeter of the gloves with the rest of the bias binding. For a special touch, sew cotton fringing around the gloves.

$\mathcal{T}$HE CUSTOM of scenting baths goes back to Roman times when handfuls of fresh lavender were thrown into bath water both to perfume and disinfect. Bathing can be a luxurious experience – Cleopatra is famous for having bathed in asses' milk, surely the ultimate luxury aid for softening and conditioning the skin. In the recipe given here spicily scented fennel acts as a stimulant, while marigold has well-known healing properties.

MARIGOLD AND FENNEL MILK BATH

MATERIALS

25 cm (10 in) butter muslin

120 ml (8 tablespoons) whole milk powder

115 g (4 oz) dried fennel seeds

55 g (2 oz) dried marigold flowers

Narrow ribbon in assorted colours

$\mathcal{T}$he marigold flower like bright little sunbursts scattered about the garden possesses healing qualities that greatly exceed its humble appearance.

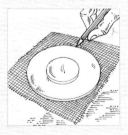

1 Cut out a circle of muslin roughly 25 cm (10 in) in diameter. For ease, draw around an upturned plate.

2 In a bowl mix together the whole milk powder, fennel seeds and marigold flowers.

3 Put a large handful of the mixture into the centre of the muslin circle. Gather up the edges to form a pouch shape. Tie tightly at the top with the ribbon, adding a long loop if you wish to hang the milk bath beneath the hot tap.

ORANGE SACHETS

*T*HESE CHARMING little fragrant sachets are prettily edged in lace and loosely filled with spicy orange peel and dried chamomile, perhaps gathered from the edges of a cornfield. They will subtly impart their gentle perfume to your freshly laundered table linen.

ORANGE PEEL AND CHAMOMILE SACHETS

MATERIALS

60 g (2 oz) dried chamomile flowerheads

115 g (4 oz) dried orange peel

Small basin

Scissors

2 lengths of 20 cm (8 in) Victorian print cotton lawn

Needle and matching thread

Variety of lace for edging

Assorted ribbons for decorative bows

1 Put the chamomile and orange peel into a small basin and mix together thoroughly. Cut two identical pieces of cotton material in each of a square and diamond shape, no more than 10 cm (4 in) wide.

2 Turn the right sides together and hand or machine stitch around the edge. Leave a 4 cm (1½ in) gap. Turn the sachets the right way round and loosely stuff them with the mixture of flowers and peel.

3 Close the gap neatly and sew the lace around the sachets by hand. Take care at the corners, making sure the lace lies flat. For the finishing touch, sew on pretty little tightly tied bows in complementary colours.

WINTER WREATH

A TRADITIONAL winter wreath made from glossy bay leaves and dried citrus fruits will add a festive note to your winter celebrations.

MATERIALS

Large bunch of small sprays of bay
Smaller bunch of rosemary or curry herb
Reel of fine florists' wire
Secateurs
Wire ring
Dried orange rings
Natural raffia

Drink to me only with thine eyes
And I will pledge with mine
Or leave a kiss but in the cup
And I'll not look for wine …
… I sent thee late a rosy wreath
Not so much honouring thee
As giving it a hope that there
It could not wither'd be;

BEN JONSON 1574–1637

1 Gather the bay and rosemary or curry herb into little bunches and bind together with florists' wire. Trim the stems with secateurs.

2 Place the bunches, all facing the same way, overlapping each other onto the wire ring. Bind with florists' wire to secure.

3 Continue adding the bunches until the whole ring is covered. Thread some citrus fruit onto a length of natural raffia and tie onto the wreath at intervals with the raffia, leaving an untidy bow to show at the front.

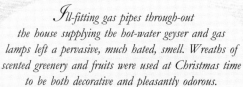

Ill-fitting gas pipes through-out the house supplying the hot-water geyser and gas lamps left a pervasive, much hated, smell. Wreaths of scented greenery and fruits were used at Christmas time to be both decorative and pleasantly odorous.

CECILIA CAVENDISH

SCENTED GARLAND

*F*OR A SPECIAL occasion, drape this gracious summer scented garland over a fireplace or ornate mirror frame.

MATERIALS

Ball of string

Assortment of summer flowers, such as jasmine (dried or fresh) and bay leaves

Reel of fine florists' wire

1 m (3 ft) wired ribbon.

1 Tie a loop at one end of the string, which has been cut to the required length.

2 Lay a small bunch of mixed flowers and leaves onto the string and bind tightly with fine florists' wire to secure.

3 Continue adding more small bunches, each one overlapping. Make sure the garland is completely covered with flowers, front and back.

4 When the garland is the required length, secure the wire. Make another loop of string for hanging the garland.

5 Finish by adding a wired ribbon bow, attaching it by wire at both ends.

*W*hen daisies pied and violets blue, And lady smocks all silver white, And cuckoo buds of yellow hue, Do paint the meadows with delight.

'Spring', Love's Labour's Lost
WILLIAM SHAKESPEARE
1564–1616

SPARKLING ELDERFLOWER

$\mathcal{A}$lthough the butler of the house was responsible for the wine cellar, it was the housekeeper who made the English wines, cordials and syrups, with locally grown ingredients. Here is a recipe for a sparkling elderflower drink that is perfect for summer parties.

INGREDIENTS

6 large heads of elderflowers

Large plastic bucket or similar container

2 lemons

1 kg (2 lb) white sugar

45 ml (3 tablespoons) white wine vinegar

5 litres (9 pt) water

Fine sieve

1 *Pick the large heads of elderflowers on a dry day, when they are in full bloom.*

2 *In a large container put the flowerheads and the juice of 2 lemons, plus the pared rind (discard the bitter white pith). Add the sugar and vinegar, and stir.*

3 *Add 5 litres (9 pt) of cold water and leave for 24 hours. Stir occasionally.*

4 *Strain the liquid through a fine sieve into a large jug.*

5 *Decant into strong bottles. Push the cork well in, and leave for 14 days. After two weeks, the drink will be sparkling and ready to enjoy.*

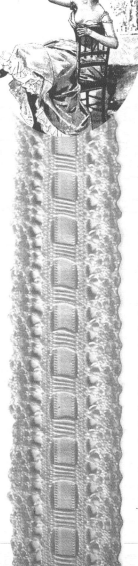

ELDERFLOWER CORDIAL

$\mathcal{E}$lderflowers and elderberries, cowslips and gooseberries were just a few of the favourite ingredients for home-made drinks. Dilute this cordial for a refreshing summer drink or pour over freshly picked strawberries.

INGREDIENTS

500 g (1 lb) freshly picked elderflowers

500 g (1 lb) white sugar

500 ml (³⁄4 pt) water

Large plastic bucket

Clean cloth (tea towel)

Saucepan

Fine sieve

Jug

Sterilized bottle with screw top

1 *Gather elderflowers on a dry sunny day. It is said to be best to pick them in the early morning.*

2 *Boil up the sugar and water until the sugar has dissolved.*

3 *Pour this syrup over the flowers in the bucket. Mix well, cover with a clean cloth and leave for 24 hours.*

4 *Put this mixture into the saucepan and simmer for 15 minutes.*

5 *Remove the elderflowers, squeeze out the syrup and bring to the boil. Then turn the heat down and simmer the liquid for 10 minutes. Allow to cool slightly.*

6 *Strain the liquid through a fine sieve into a clean jug. Pour into a hot sterilized bottle, right up to the top, leaving no air space. Screw the lid on tightly. This cordial needs to be stored in the refrigerator and consumed within a month.*